It's another Quality Book from CGP

This book is for anyone doing AQA GCSE Food Technology.

It contains lots of tricky questions just like the ones that could come up in the exam. They're designed to make you sweat — because that's the only way you'll get any better.

It's also got a few daft bits in to try and make the whole experience at least vaguely entertaining for you.

What CGP is all about

Our sole aim here at CGP is to produce the highest quality books — carefully written, immaculately presented and dangerously close to being funny.

Then we work our socks off to get them out to you — at the cheapest possible prices.

Contents

Exam Advice 1

SECTION ONE — THE DESIGN PROCESS

Product and Market Analysis 4

Market Research 6

Design Criteria 9

Generating Proposals 10

Product Specification 13

Development 15

Manufacturer's Specification 18

SECTION TWO — PROPERTIES OF FOOD

Carbohydrates — Sugar 20

Carbohydrates — Starch 21

Proteins — Meat, Poultry and Fish 23

Proteins — Eggs 24

Fats and Oils 26

Vitamins and Minerals 28

Additives 30

Acids and Alkalis 32

Healthy Eating 34

New Technology 36

SECTION THREE — FOOD PROCESSES

Combining Ingredients 38

Standard Food Components 40

Scale of Production 42

Quality Control 44

Food Contamination and Bacteria 46

Preservation 48

Domestic and Industrial Equipment 50

SECTION FOUR — MARKETING AND ENVIRONMENT

Social Issues 52

Environmental Issues 54

Labelling 56

Packaging 58

Published by CGP

Editors:
Katie Braid, Rosie Gillham and Sarah Williams

Contributors:
Nicole Billinge, Gemma Hallam, Caley Simpson and Charlotte Tweedy

With thanks to Susan Hey for the content review.
With thanks to Katherine Craig and Phil Holden for the proofreading.

With thanks to Laura Stoney for the copyright research.

ISBN: 978 1 84762 394 2

Groovy website: www.cgpbooks.co.uk
Jolly bits of clipart from CorelDRAW®

With thanks to iStockphoto® for permission to use the biscuit cutter image on page 51.

Printed by Elanders Ltd, Newcastle upon Tyne.

Based on the classic CGP style created by Richard Parsons.

Exam Advice

The Exam Paper is in Two Sections

1) There's <u>one exam</u> for AQA Food Technology and it's split into <u>two sections</u> — Section A and Section B.

2) You need to answer <u>all of the questions</u> in both sections.

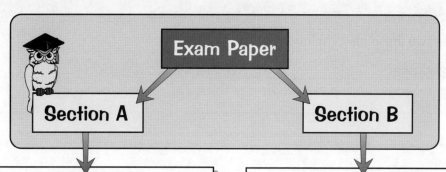

Section A is the <u>design</u> question. The questions in Section A will all be on the same theme, e.g. snack products sold in a tuck shop. You'll be asked to sketch out some <u>design ideas</u>, then <u>develop</u> one of them into a final design — it's the place in the exam for showing that you can come up with <u>original</u> and <u>creative</u> ideas.

Section B covers <u>everything</u> you've learnt about in your Food Technology course — how to design things, properties of food, food processes, health and safety, environmental issues... There'll be a mixture of <u>short</u> and <u>longer</u> answer questions, as well as some <u>sketching</u> and some <u>tables</u> to fill in.

A little while before the exam, your teacher will give you a <u>Preparation Sheet</u>. This gives you the <u>theme</u> of the Section A question — use it to do some <u>research</u> into the theme.

3) The exam lasts for <u>2 hours</u>. Each question will have a suggestion of how long you should spend on it. Try to follow this — it really will help you to have a good go at every question.

4) One of your answers will be assessed for <u>quality of written communication</u> — that's spelling, punctuation and grammar, as well as how clear your answer is. You'll be <u>told</u> which question this is on the front of the exam paper — so read all that information carefully and put a <u>note</u> to yourself next to the relevant question.

There are a Few Golden Rules

1) Always, always, always make sure you <u>read the question</u> properly. For example, if the question asks you to sketch <u>three</u> design ideas, make sure you do three — <u>not two, not four</u>. And don't <u>waste loads of time</u> making them really neat — they're only supposed to be sketches. (There are places where you do need to be really neat though — drawing graphs and charts, or a final design idea.)

2) It's a good idea to <u>underline</u> the important bits of the question. Then you can keep checking to make sure you're not going off track and waffling about stuff that's not going to get you any marks.

3) Pay attention to the <u>number of marks</u> a question is worth — if it's worth three marks, give three good points. And try to <u>fill</u> most of the space available for the answer. If there are three lines and you've only filled one, you probably haven't written enough.

4) Always use the right <u>technical words</u> — words like 'roux' and 'coagulation' make examiners happy.

5) Make your answers as <u>specific</u> as possible. If you're asked to suggest a target group, don't just write people with special diets — give a specific type of diet, e.g. vegetarian.

Exam Advice

You Need to Understand the Command Words

Command words are the words in a question that tell you what to do — describe, explain, etc.
If you don't know what they mean, you won't be able to answer the questions properly. Boo hiss.

Name...

If you're asked to name something just say what it's called — you don't need to give any extra information.

6   a)   Name **two** finishing techniques.

1. ...glazing...

2. ...icing...

(2 marks)

Give...

You just need to write down the answer — you don't need to explain it.

2   Additives are substances added to food products to improve their properties.

a)   Give **one** example of each of the following types of additives.

i)   A raising agent.

bicarbonate of soda..

(1 mark)

Describe...

Describing means picking out the features — of, say, a process. If you're asked to just 'briefly describe' something you don't need to go into too much detail.

4   It is important to consider safety and hygiene at all stages of food production.

a)   Describe the safety and hygiene precautions that you should take when purchasing food.

You should always buy food from a reputable supplier. You should make sure

the food is fresh by checking the use by date. You should also check the food

carefully to make sure it hasn't been squashed or gone mouldy, and that the

packaging isn't damaged.

(3 marks)

Explain...

If you're asked to explain something, you need to give reasons — don't just write out what it is.

3   b)   Explain why strong flour is the most suitable flour to use when making bread.

Strong flour has a high gluten content, which is needed to give the dough

its elasticity. Gluten helps the bread to rise and have a light, airy texture.

(3 marks)

Exam Advice

Evaluate... You need to weigh something up — here you need to compare your idea to the specification and decide whether you've covered each point.

1 b) The design specification for a children's birthday cake has the following points:
- The cake must be suitable for a young child.
- The cake must be suitable for people with nut allergies.

Evaluate your design idea against the design specification above.

The bright colours, icing and fun decorations will appeal to young children.

The cake will be made using ingredients that do not contain any nuts or traces

of nuts, and so will be suitable for people with nut allergies.

(2 marks)

Analyse... Analysing is picking out and evaluating the features of something. Here you'd have to say whether the features of the sausages make them suitable for their target market.

7 Analyse this design idea for alternative protein sausages.
Comment on whether you think the design is suitable for its target market.

rosemary & garlic Quorn™ sausages

The sausages are designed to appeal to vegetarians or other people who choose not to eat meat sausages. It should attract the target market as the sausages are meat-free but contain Quorn™ so are high in protein. The sausages are flavoured to make them more appealing to consumers.

(3 marks)

Annotate... Annotate means adding notes. This could be to label or explain a feature on a sketch

5 Sketch a design idea for a sandwich suitable for a consumer following a low calorie diet.
Annotate your sketch to show how your design idea meets this design criteria.

Thin sliced bread. Bread is high in carbohydrates, so using less bread means the sandwich will have fewer calories.

No butter or margarine. These would add calories and aren't needed for moisture with a cottage cheese filling.

Cottage cheese. This is a low fat filling so has fewer calories than many other sandwich fillings.

Salad. This adds flavour, texture, it makes the sandwich look appealing and it is low in calories.

(4 marks)

Product and Market Analysis — 1

1 All food packaging must show the product's ingredients.

Give **two** other examples of information found on food packaging.

1. cost of the product

2. cooking instructions

(2 marks)

2 Products are usually designed for a particular **target group**.

a) Explain what is meant by the term 'target group'.

Group of people the company want to sell the product to

(1 mark)

b) Suggest **one** way in which a product could be designed to appeal to the following target groups:

i) vegetarians

not contain meat

(1 mark)

ii) people with busy lifestyles

quick to prepare

(1 mark)

3 A company is doing some research into healthy snack bars.
Two existing products are shown below.

Snack A

healthy, fruity &
delicious low sugar high fibre 0% fat

Snack B

super fruity
snackeroony free sticker inside

a) State which of the snacks shown is targeted at young children.

Snack B

(1 mark)

b) Suggest a target group for the other snack. Give a detailed reason for your answer.

adults and people who are on a diet,
the product has a sensible name
nutritional content.

(3 marks)

Product and Market Analysis — 2

4 A cereal company plans to design a new product, aimed specifically at children.
Before they design their product they analyse two **existing** children's cereals, shown below.

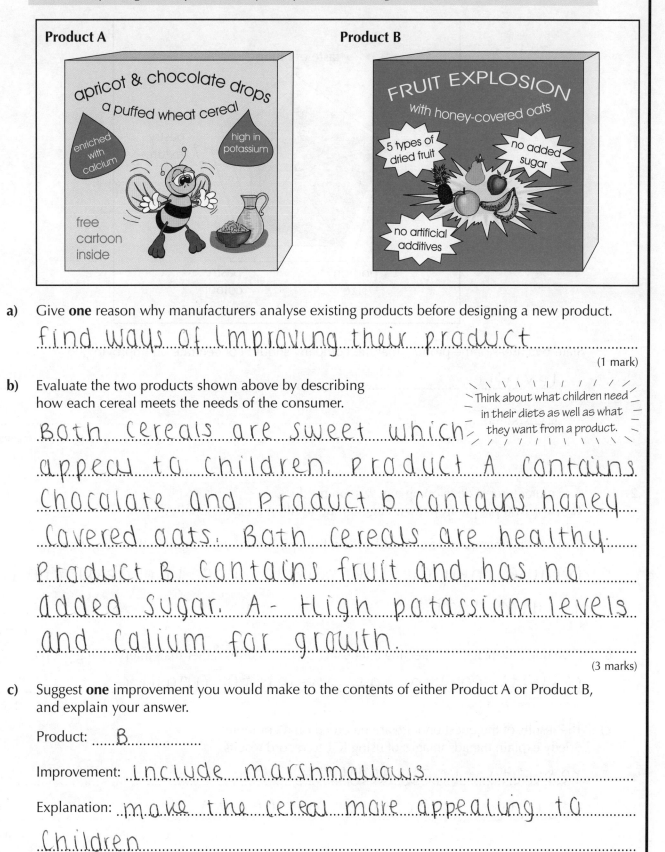

Product A

apricot & chocolate drops

a puffed wheat cereal

enriched with calcium

high in potassium

free cartoon inside

Product B

FRUIT EXPLOSION

with honey-covered oats

5 types of dried fruit

no added sugar

no artificial additives

a) Give **one** reason why manufacturers analyse existing products before designing a new product.

find ways of improving their product

(1 mark)

b) Evaluate the two products shown above by describing
how each cereal meets the needs of the consumer.

~Think about what children need
in their diets as well as what
they want from a product.

Both cereals are sweet which
appeal to children. Product A contains
chocolate and product b contains honey
covered oats. Both cereals are healthy.
Product B contains fruit and has no
added sugar. A- High potassium levels
and calium for growth.

(3 marks)

c) Suggest **one** improvement you would make to the contents of either Product A or Product B,
and explain your answer.

Product: .....B...........

Improvement: ...include marshmallows...........

Explanation: ...make the cereal more appealing to......
Children

(2 marks)

<u>Market Research — 1</u>

1 A pie company conducted a sensory analysis test on a new chicken and mushroom pie.
The results are presented below in a star diagram.

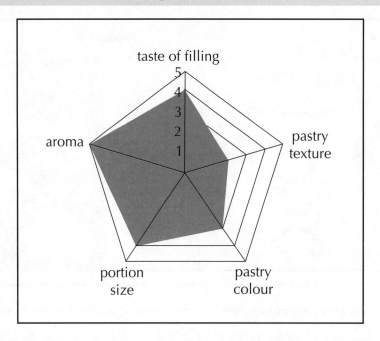

State **two** areas of the product that the company should concentrate on improving.

1. <u>texture</u>

2. <u>colour</u>

(2 marks)

2 A manufacturer is developing a new soup product.
They ask 100 people from their target group to fill in a questionnaire.

a) Explain why manufacturers should collect the opinions of the people in their target group.

<u>Because they are the people who the new product</u>
<u>is aimed at</u>

(2 marks)

b) Give **one** advantage of collecting data using questionnaires rather than interviewing people.

<u>results can be ~~its~~ easier to analyse</u>

(1 mark)

c) The results of the questionnaire are recorded on a computer.
Briefly explain the advantages of using ICT to record results.

<u>results look neater</u>
<u>results can easily be copied</u>

(2 marks)

Section One — The Design Process

Market Research — 2

3   The graph below shows the results of a **difference test** for a low-fat yogurt.
100 testers were asked to identify the low-fat yogurt from a sample of three yogurts.

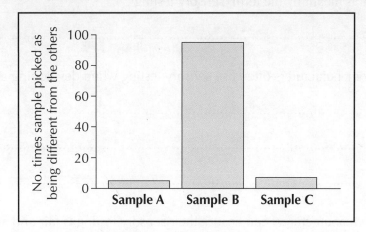

The low-fat yogurt was Sample B. Explain why the company might choose to re-design the yogurt.

tell the difference between the low fat yogurt and the full fat yogurt

(2 marks)

4   A company is developing a new type of cheesecake. They conduct a **ranking test** to see how their product performs against three other cheesecakes. The overall results are shown below.

Product	Order of Preference
A	2
B	1
C	4
D	3

a)   The company's cheesecake is Product A.
Suggest how the company could use the results of the ranking test to make their product better.

Improve their product to be more like Product B

(2 marks)

b)   Explain how a **rating test** is different from a ranking test.

Involves asking people to give each product a rating

(2 marks)

Market Research — 3

5 Manufacturers use a range of sensory testing methods when developing new products.

a) Explain what is meant by the term 'sensory testing'.

....

(1 mark)

b) Explain why manufacturers often use sensory testing when developing a product.

....

....

....

(3 marks)

c) Suggest how manufacturers can ensure their sensory testing is fair and accurate.

....

....

....

(3 marks)

6 Two types of pastry were tested for their suitability for sausage rolls. The results are shown below. Analyse the results and suggest how they could be used by a sausage roll manufacturer.

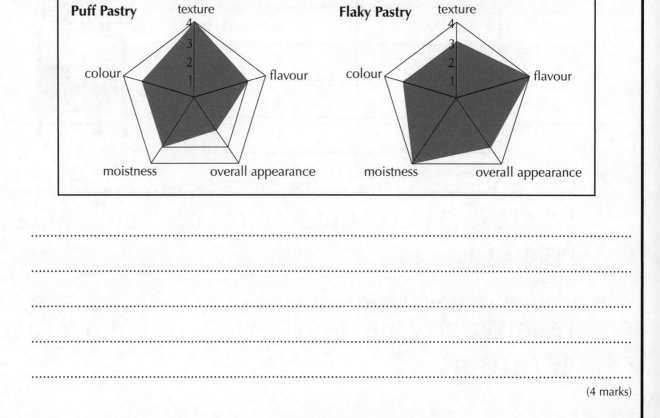

....

....

....

....

....

(4 marks)

Design Criteria

1   A ready-meal manufacturer wants to produce a new rice dish. Their **design brief** is shown below.

> **CONTEXT:** A ready-made rice-based dish to be cooked at home.
>
> **TARGET MARKET:** Consumers with busy lifestyles.
>
> **PRODUCT TO BE DEVELOPED:** A rice-based product.

Give **three** pieces of information that the manufacturer should research to be able to develop a successful product.

1. ....

2. ....

3. ....

(3 marks)

2   The extract below is a summary of a company's research into **savoury snacks**.

> "Most people prefer potato crisps to rice-based snacks. Flavour and texture were the most important factors for consumers. The more exotic snack flavours, such as Thai Curry and Moroccan Chicken, scored highest in sensory tests. Potato crisps scored higher than rice-based snacks for texture. Consumers were concerned about health and nutrition — they wanted the product to be low in calories and high in nutrients. Most people were willing to spend about 50p on a serving."

Write **four** design criteria for a savoury snack based on this research summary.

1. ....

2. ....

3. ....

4. ....

(4 marks)

3   Write **three** design criteria for a savoury product designed to go in a child's lunchbox.

....

....

....

(3 marks)

Generating Proposals — 1

1 A designer has produced two ideas for a take-away savoury snack. Study the **design criteria** and the two **design ideas** below.

Idea 1
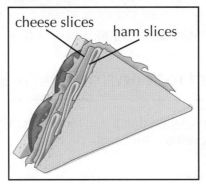
cheese slices, ham slices

Idea 2

melted cheese, mushroom slices

Design Criteria

A successful product will be:
- cheap to produce
- low in fat
- high in protein
- suitable to eat without a plate or cutlery

Which of the two design ideas should be developed? Idea 1 ☐   Idea 2 ☐

Explain your answer.

....

(2 marks)

2 The design criteria and initial design proposal for a **vegan** chocolate bar are shown below.

Design criteria:
- must contain nuts
- must be cheap
- must be low in sugar
- must be free from dairy products

Initial design proposal:

luxury Belgian milk chocolate
caramel filling in the centre
sugar-coated nuts

a) Evaluate the initial design proposal against the design criteria.

....

....

....

....

(4 marks)

b) Suggest **three** modifications that would improve the design so that it matches the criteria.

1. ....

2. ....

3. ....

(3 marks)

Section One — The Design Process

Generating Proposals — 2

3   You have been asked to develop a new soup product.

The product should:
- have a smooth texture
- suit batch production
- contain at least one portion of vegetables
- suit consumers with a special dietary requirement
- offer sensory appeal

a)   Use notes and/or sketches to produce **one** design idea for a soup product.

(6 marks)

b)   Explain how nutritional analysis software could be useful when designing a soup.

....

....

....

....

(3 marks)

Section One — The Design Process

Generating Proposals — 3

4   A bakery is developing a new range of pastry products.

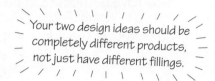
Your two design ideas should be completely different products, not just have different fillings.

The product should:
- have a savoury filling
- appeal to vegetarian consumers
- have a glazed finish
- offer sensory appeal

Use notes and/or annotated sketches to produce **two** different design ideas that meet the design criteria for the pastry product. Do **not** draw any packaging.

Idea 1

(5 marks)

Idea 2

(5 marks)

Product Specification — 1

1   This question is about product specifications.

a)   Explain what is meant by a 'product specification'.

expands on your chosen idea

(1 mark)

b)   Explain why it is important to evaluate design ideas against the design criteria during their development.

how it will look & taste

(2 marks)

c)   Suggest **one** way a company could check their product specification meets a product's design criteria.

compare to desgin criteria

(1 mark)

2   A new food product idea can be **protected** by registering it as intellectual property. Explain why a company might want to protect a product design.

no one can steal their idea if it has been registered. They can make money from their idea

(2 marks)

3   Examine the product specification for a low-sugar biscuit below.

> 1.   Each biscuit might weigh about 100 g.
> 2.   Biscuits must be low in sugar.
> 3.   The cost of making the biscuits shouldn't be too expensive.

Write an **improved version** of the product specification for the low-sugar biscuit.

1. *manufacturing cost of each biscuit*
2. *weight*
3. *Sugar*

(3 marks)

Product Specification — 2

4   Study the **design criteria** below for a pasta-based product.

The product should:
- be a savoury meal for one person
- have a tomato-based sauce
- be high in carbohydrate
- be high in protein
- offer sensory appeal

Make sure you point out how your idea meets all these design criteria.

a)   Use notes and/or annotated sketches to produce **one** design idea that meets the design criteria for the pasta-based product.

(5 marks)

b)   Write a **five**-point product specification for your design idea.

1. ....

2. ....

3. ....

4. ....

5. ....

(5 marks)

Development — 1

1 A company wants to make a cheaper version of their luxury chicken sandwich.

a) Suggest **one** way in which the company could reduce the cost of producing the sandwich.

decrease portion size

(1 mark)

b) Give **one** disadvantage of the change you suggested in part **a)**.

might have to be sold at a lower price

(1 mark)

2 A cake manufacturer is developing a new sponge cake. Their latest model has failed a sensory test for texture. The testers thought that the sponge was too dry.

Describe **two** ways of developing the sponge cake recipe to improve its texture.

Use more fat in the cake

Reduce the cooking time

(2 marks)

3 A basic apple crumble can be made using the following ingredients:

- 500 g cooking apples
- 150 g granulated sugar
- 100 g plain flour
- 75 g butter
- 50 g caster sugar

Describe how the apple crumble recipe can be developed to meet the needs of:

a) consumers with coeliac disease,

use gluten free flour

(1 mark)

b) consumers requiring more vitamin C in their diet.

Increase the proportion of apples

(1 mark)

Development — 2

4 A manufacturer of pre-made chilli meals decides to adapt a product to make it suitable for consumers on a **calorie-controlled diet**. They do this by reducing the portion size of the meal.

a) Give **two** other ways of adapting the chilli product to make it suitable for consumers on a calorie-controlled diet.

use lower fat ingredients
healthier cooking method

(2 marks)

b) The manufacturer produces a model of the adapted chilli, but the chilli produced is burnt. Suggest **two** adjustments that could be made to the production process to solve this problem.

reduce cooking time and cooking
temperature

(2 marks)

c) Explain why modelling a product is an important part of the development process.

manufacturer to discover and solve any
potential problems.

(2 marks)

5 A healthy flapjack product has the following design criteria:

> • low in sugar
> • low in fat
> • sweet taste
> • moist, chewy texture
> • contain rolled oats

Nutritional analysis and market research show the current recipe uses too much fat and sugar to be marketed as 'healthy'. The recipe is altered to use **less golden syrup** and **less butter**.

a) Describe how these changes to the recipe might affect how well the flapjack meets the design criteria.

taste might be affected by using less
golden syrup.

(3 marks)

b) Suggest how the company could develop the flapjack so that it still meets all the design criteria.

use low-sugar golden syrup. low fat spread

(1 mark)

Development — 3

6   100 people were interviewed on their cake preferences. The results are shown below.

Preferred flavour:

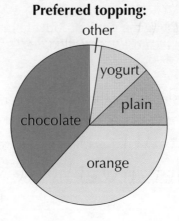

Preferred topping:

Most important feature:

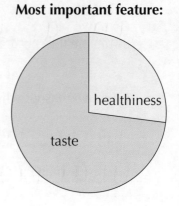

a)   Using these results, sketch and annotate a design idea for a cake product.

(3 marks)

b)   Analyse your design idea. Suggest how you could adapt your idea to suit the needs
of consumers with special dietary requirements due to food intolerances or allergies.

....

....

....

....

....

....

....

(4 marks)

Manufacturer's Specification — 1

1   The order of manufacturing processes in food production are often presented as flowcharts.
     Give **one** other format that the order of work can be presented in.

     in a Chart
     ....
                                                                                     (1 mark)

2   Give **two** reasons why you should test the manufacturer's specification in a test kitchen.

     Instructions are clear and detailed
     final product meets design criteria
                                                                                     (2 marks)

3   Look at this working drawing for a salami and cheese salad sandwich.

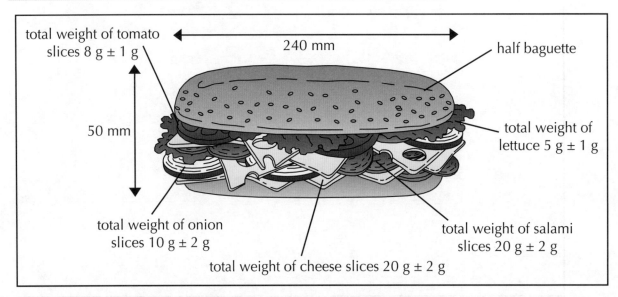

     total weight of tomato slices 8 g ± 1 g

     240 mm

     half baguette

     50 mm

     total weight of lettuce 5 g ± 1 g

     total weight of onion slices 10 g ± 2 g

     total weight of cheese slices 20 g ± 2 g

     total weight of salami slices 20 g ± 2 g

   a) State the maximum weight of cheese that can be used in the sandwich.

     22g
     ....
                                                                                     (1 mark)

   b) State whether the drawing above provides enough information for it to be considered
       a full manufacturing specification. Give a reason for your answer.

     doesn't provide enough information
     doesn't include castings
                                                                                     (2 marks)

   c) Explain how manufacturing the sandwich in bulk will affect the cost per unit,
       compared to making just one sandwich.

     make it cheaper
     Production lines can be cheaper
                                                                                     (2 marks)

Manufacturers's Specification — 2

4 A **manufacturer's specification** provides the information needed to produce large quantities of a product. List **three** details a manufacturer's specification should include.

1. List of Ingredients with precise amounts

2. Quality control Instructions

3. Costings

(3 marks)

5 Complete the flowchart below to produce a plan for making a chicken and lettuce sandwich from sliced bread, oil, butter, raw chicken and lettuce. Include control checks in your flowchart.

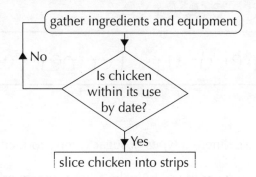

gather ingredients and equipment

No

Is chicken within its use by date?

Yes

slice chicken into strips

Think of all the steps you'd need to make yourself this sandwich.

(6 marks)

Carbohydrates — Sugar

1 Sugar has many functions in cooking.

a) When heated, sugar forms a brownish liquid that can be used to decorate desserts.
Give the name of this process.

Caramelisation

(1 mark)

b) State **one** function of the sugar used in each product below. An example has been done for you.

Food Product		Function
E.g.	Biscuits	To add colour.
	Jam	to preserve
	Bread	Speed up fermentation

(2 marks)

2 Manufacturers often use different types of sugar when producing cakes.

a) Name the most suitable sugar to use to **make** a light sponge cake.
Give **one** reason for your choice.

Caster Sugar- it will give the sponge a
smooth texture.

(2 marks)

b) Name the most suitable sugar to use to **decorate** a cake. Give **one** reason for your choice.

icing Sugar- it instantly dissolves in
water to form a smooth paste.

(2 marks)

3 Soft drinks are often high in sugar.

a) State **one** nutritional property of sugar.

Provides energy

(1 mark)

b) Suggest **two** reasons why a soft drinks manufacturer might choose
to use artificial sweeteners instead of sugar in their products.

To appeal to people with diabetes.
appeal to consumers who want a better drink
for their teeth.

(2 marks)

Carbohydrates — Starch — 1

1   Starch is a type of carbohydrate.

a)   Give **two** ingredients or foods that are high in starch.

flour and pasta

(2 marks)

b)   What is the nutritional value of starch?

Provides energy

(1 mark)

2   A basic macaroni cheese is made up from pasta, white sauce and cheese.
Explain the **function** of starch in each of these components:

Component	Function of Starch
Pasta	*starch acts as a bulking agent.*
White sauce	*starch acts as a thickening agent*

(4 marks)

3   Many manufacturers use modified starches in their products.

> Modified starches are also known as 'smart' starches.

a)   **i)**   Explain what is meant by the term 'modified starch'.

Starch that has been treated so that it reacts in a particular way in certain conditions

(1 mark)

    ii)   Give **one** advantage of using pre-gelatinised starch in an instant noodle product.

Starch has already gelatinised

(1 mark)

b)   When protein is heated it coagulates, squeezing fat and water out of food in a process called
syneresis. Some modified starches prevent syneresis from occurring when products are reheated.
Explain the advantages of using modified starches in frozen products like lasagne.

food will keep its moisture and nutrients when reheated

(2 marks)

Carbohydrates — Starch — 2

4 A basic bread dough is made from flour, water, yeast and salt.

a) **i)** Name the type of flour most suitable to use in bread-making.

....

(1 mark)

ii) Name the protein in bread dough that makes it elastic.

....

(1 mark)

iii) Describe the function of the yeast in bread dough.

....

(1 mark)

b) Suggest **one** ingredient that could be added to bread dough to change the flavour of the final product.

....

(1 mark)

c) Using notes and/or annotated sketches, design a **savoury** bread product that could be sold at a take-away snack stall. The product should:

Annotated sketches have added notes to explain ideas.

- be suitable to be eaten as a snack 'on-the-go',
- offer sensory appeal.

(3 marks)

Proteins — Meat, Poultry and Fish

1 Meat, fish and alternative protein foods are all good sources of protein.

a) Give **one** example of: **i)** red meat ....

                   ii) white meat ....

                   iii) fish ....

                   iv) an alternative protein food ....

(4 marks)

b) Explain why protein is essential in a person's diet.

....

....

....

(3 marks)

2 Describe **two** methods of tenderising meat before cooking.

....

....

(2 marks)

3 Using notes and/or annotated sketches, design **one** meal suitable for a **vegetarian**.

The product should: • be savoury,
                      • be high in protein,
                      • provide sensory appeal.

(4 marks)

Proteins — Eggs — 1

1   Bread products are often glazed before they are baked.

a)   Describe the process of glazing.

....

(1 mark)

b)   Give **one** reason why a manufacturer might glaze their products.

....

(1 mark)

2   Eggs are a high protein food.

Name **three** other nutrients
found in eggs.

1.   ....

2.   ....

3.   ....

(3 marks)

3   A café serves a full English breakfast made up of sausages, bacon and eggs, all fried in butter.

a)   Explain why fried eggs are considered to be unhealthy.

....

(1 mark)

b)   Describe **two** ways the chef at the café could make the fried eggs they serve healthier.

....

....

....

(2 marks)

c)   Give **two** other methods of cooking eggs that are healthier than frying.

1.   ....

2.   ....

(2 marks)

Proteins — Eggs — 2

4 Eggs have various functions in cooking. Complete the table below by describing the **function** of the egg in the different foods listed. An example has been done for you.

	Food	Function of the Egg	Description
E.g.	Burgers	Binding	Eggs coagulate and stick the ingredients together as they cook.
	Quiche	Coagulation	....
	Mayonnaise	Emulsification	....
	Cake	Aeration	....

(6 marks)

6 marks for 3 answers usually means you'll get 2 marks for each.

5 Eggs can cause food poisoning if they are not properly prepared.

a) Name **one** bacteria found in raw eggs that can cause food poisoning.

....

(1 mark)

b) Describe **two** precautions a manufacturer may take when using eggs in their products.

....

....

....

(2 marks)

Fats and Oils — 1

1   Fat can be saturated or unsaturated.

a)   Name **one** source of saturated fat.

....
                                                                        (1 mark)

b)   Name **one** source of unsaturated fat.

....
                                                                        (1 mark)

c)   State which type of fat is thought to be healthier and explain your answer.

....

....
                                                                       (2 marks)

2   Fat is an essential ingredient in many foods. Describe the nutritional profile of a high fat food.

....

....
                                                                       (3 marks)

3   A pie company wants to improve the pastry in their products. Sensory tests have shown their pastry is too crumbly.

a)   Suggest how they could modify their recipe to improve the pastry texture. Give a detailed reason for your answer.

....

....

....
                                                          (3 marks)

b)   The company wants the top of their pie to be golden-yellow in colour. Name **one** type of fat that could be added to the pastry mixture to get this appearance.

....
                                                                        (1 mark)

c)   Give **one** other function of fats and oils when making pastry.

....
                                                                        (1 mark)

d)   The pies are filled with a creamy mushroom sauce. Suggest **one** reason why cream is used in the sauce.

....
                                                                         (1 mark)

Fats and Oils — 2

4 Fish and chip shops use fats to fry chips.

a) Suggest **two** reasons why chip shops may choose to use lard to cook chips.

....

....

(2 marks)

b) Explain why chips cooked in lard would **not** be suitable for vegetarians.

....

....

(2 marks)

c) Name **one** alternative fat that the chips could be cooked in to make them suitable for vegetarians **and** vegans.

....

(1 mark)

5 Sales of lard have changed dramatically during the twentieth century. The table below shows lard sales in the UK over a 50-year period.

Year	1950s	1960s	1970s	1980s	1990s
Sales of lard	£48.5 million	£42.7 million	£35.4 million	£23.7 million	£12.9 million

a) Using the information shown in the table, describe how the sales of lard have changed since the 1950s.

....

(1 mark)

b) Based on the sales figures for lard since the 1950s, suggest **three** possible reasons for this trend in the UK.

....

....

....

....

....

....

(3 marks)

Vitamins and Minerals — 1

1   Vegetarians can find it hard to get enough iron in their diet.

a)   Name **one** vegetarian food rich in iron.

....

(1 mark)

b)   Briefly explain why iron is needed as part of a healthy diet.

....

(1 mark)

c)   Name **one** disease that can be caused by an iron deficiency.

....

(1 mark)

2   Vitamins are essential for good health. Complete the table below to show **two** sources and **one** function of each vitamin(s). The first one has been done for you as an example.

	Vitamin	Food Sources	Function in the Body
E.g.	Vitamin A	butter, eggs	Helps with the growth and function of body tissues.
	Vitamin B Group	....	....
	Vitamin C (ascorbic acid)	....	....

(6 marks)

3   A restaurant serves carrots with every main meal. They use fresh carrots, which are peeled and sliced before being cooked in boiling water.

a)   Suggest **three** ways to minimise the nutrient loss from the carrots as they are cooked.

....

....

....

(3 marks)

b)   What effect would freezing the carrots before cooking have on their nutritional value?

....

(1 mark)

Vitamins and Minerals — 2

4   Vitamin D is needed to help the body absorb calcium.

a)   Briefly explain why calcium is needed as part of a healthy diet.

....

....

(2 marks)

b)   Name **one** food that is a good source of each of the following nutrients:

i)   vitamin D

....

(1 mark)

ii)   calcium

....

(1 mark)

c)   Name **one** disease caused by vitamin D deficiency.

....

(1 mark)

5   Nutrients can be easily lost from fruit during storage and preparation.

Produce a plan for making a fruit salad using a flowchart, notes and/or diagrams.
Your fruit salad should include bananas, apples, oranges and kiwi fruits. Within your plan,
explain how you would **prepare** and **store** the fruit to minimise the loss of nutrients.

(5 marks)

Additives — 1

1   Monosodium glutamate (MSG) is a natural additive.

  a)   Give **one** reason why MSG is added to food.

it boosts the existing flavour of a product
(1 mark)

  b)   Name **one** type of food that MSG is often added to.

Crisps
(1 mark)

2   Some additives are natural and others are artificial.

  a)   Suggest **one** reason why a manufacturer might prefer to use natural additives in their products rather than artificial ones.

customers don't tend to like the idea of artificial additives, so are more likely to buy products containing natural additives.
(1 mark)

  b)   A caramel and vanilla slice contains the following ingredients:

> Flour, eggs, milk, butter, salt, jam, sugar, caramel, saccharin, vanilla essence.

  i)   Name **two** natural additives from the ingredients list.

sugar and caramel
(2 marks)

  ii)   Name **two** artificial additives from the ingredients list.

vanilla essence and saccharin
(2 marks)

  c)   Suggest **two** reasons why the additives you named in part **b)** might be used in the slice.

add flavour
(2 marks)

3   The picture on the right shows a can of soda.
The soda contains the additive sorbitol, which has the
E number E420. Describe what the term 'E number' means.

does it mean that it has
passed the safety test
(2 marks)

INGREDIENTS:
carbonated water, sugar,
citric acid, sorbitol (E420)

Additives — 2

4 The table below shows different functions of additives. Complete the table by naming an **additive** used for each function. Give an **example** of a food where the additive is used.

	Function	Additive	Example of when the additive is used in food
a)	Preservative	vinegar	Pickle foods like onions and eggs.
b)	Emulsifier	lecithin	natural emulsifier found in egg yolks. its used in products like mayonnaise and margarine
c)	Setting Agent	Gelatine	natural gelling agent thats extracted from animals - its used in desserts like mousses and jellies
d)	Raising Agent	Yeast	a biological raising agent used in bread dough. yeast are microorganisms that cause fermentation producing carbon dioxide.

(8 marks)

5 Evaluate the use of additives in food products.

'Evaluate' means you've got to weigh up the pros and cons of something.

Some people are allergic to certain additives - con. Add flavour - pro. Some additives like sugar or salt used in large can be bad for your health - con. Add colour - pro. enhance the flavour - pro. They can disguise poor quality ingredients e.g processed meat products may not contain much meat but they can be made to taste good by using additives - con.

(6 marks)

Acids and Alkalis — 1

1   A health food company produces nuts covered in yogurt as a healthy snack food.

a)   Name the **acid** that is used to make yogurt from milk.

lactic acid

(1 mark)

b)   An additive is added to the yogurt to improve the flavour.
Suggest why the flavour of the yogurt might need improving.

Because the acid will give
yogurt a sour taste

(1 mark)

2   A company is developing a fruit pavlova product.

a)   During the product development, vinegar was added to the meringue mixture.

i)   Briefly describe the effect this would have had on the meringue.
Explain how the vinegar causes this effect.

Vinegar breaks down the protein and
changes the texture

(2 marks)

ii) Suggest **two** alternative uses for vinegar in food preparation.

1. Sharp flavour
2. Preserve foods

(2 marks)

iii) Name an **alkali** that could be added to give the meringue a thicker texture.

Cornflour

(1 mark)

b)   Once the fruit for the pavlova is sliced, it is immediately put into concentrated lemon juice.
Explain why this is necessary.

the concentrated lemon juice will help the
fruit to keep its colour.

(2 marks)

Acids and Alkalis — 2

3   Alkalis are often used in cake mixtures to make cakes rise.

a) Name **one** alkali that acts as a raising agent.

Bicarbonate of soda

(1 mark)

b) Briefly explain how the alkali you named in part **a)** acts as a raising agent.

Breaks down when heated to produce carbon dioxide

(2 marks)

c) Give **one** disadvantage of using alkalis in cakes.

bad taste

(1 mark)

d) Name **two** different products it would be suitable to make using an alkaline raising agent. Explain why the disadvantage given in **c)** would not be a problem for these products.

Strong flavour of the product wan't taste nice

(3 marks)

4   Using notes and/or annotated sketches, design a dessert that makes use of at least **one acid** and **one alkali**. Clearly identify the acid and alkali used, and explain their functions in your dessert.

(5 marks)

Healthy Eating — 1

1   Explain what the Government's 'Five a Day' guideline means.

....

....

....

(1 mark)

2   Look at the extract from a food diary shown below.

> **Tuesday**   Breakfast: 2 pieces of toast with margarine
>   1 glass of orange juice
>
>   Lunch: 75 g of cheese, melted on two pieces of toast
>
>   Dinner: steak pie and a portion of chips
>
>   Additional snacks: 1 chocolate bar (30 g)
>   1 packet of crisps (35 g)

Whenever you're asked about diet, think about the Eatwell plate.

a)   Suggest **two** ways in which the person keeping the diary
     could improve their diet.

....

....

(2 marks)

b)   The person keeping the food diary is diabetic. Name **one** food listed that they should avoid eating.

....

(1 mark)

3   Name **one** health problem linked with eating an excess of the following nutrients:

a)   salt

....

(1 mark)

b)   fat

....

(1 mark)

c)   sugar

....

(1 mark)

Healthy Eating — 2

4 A basic spaghetti bolognese is made up of spaghetti, mince and a tomato-based sauce, served with grated cheese on top.

a) Describe different ways in which the spaghetti bolognese could be adapted for:

i) a consumer who follows a vegan diet,

....

....
(2 marks)

ii) a consumer with coeliac disease,

....
(1 mark)

iii) a consumer with nut allergies.

....
(1 mark)

b) Some people need to avoid drinking cow's milk and eating dairy products.

i) What is the name given to this condition?

....
(1 mark)

ii) Identify **one** ingredient in the spaghetti bolognese that they would be unable to eat.

....
(1 mark)

5 A basic swiss roll is made from sponge cake, jam and cream. Describe how a basic swiss roll product could be adapted to meet the needs of a consumer on a **calorie-controlled diet**. You may use annotated sketches in your answer.

(3 marks)

New Technology — 1

1   GM foods are produced using new technologies.

a)   State what 'GM' stands for.

....

(1 mark)

b)   Briefly describe what is meant by a GM food.

....

....

(2 marks)

2   Some people are worried about eating GM foods.

a)   State **two** potential concerns consumers have about GM products.

....

....

(2 marks)

b)   The EU has strict safety laws on GM foods. State **one** of these laws.

....

(1 mark)

3   The photograph below shows a bag of ready-prepared salad.
It is packaged using modified atmosphere packaging (MAP) to extend its shelf life.

Give **one** other example of how technology can be used to extend the shelf life of a product.

....

....

(1 mark)

New Technology — 2

4   New technologies have allowed manufacturers to develop **functional foods**.

a)   Explain what is meant by the term 'functional food'.

....

....

(2 marks)

b)   Give **two** examples of functional foods.

1. ....

2. ....

(2 marks)

c)   Describe how functional foods can improve people's health.

....

....

....

....

(3 marks)

5   Evaluate the advantages and disadvantages of **producing** GM products.

For longer exam questions like this, make sure you write in full sentences and check your spelling and grammar.

....

....

....

....

....

....

....

....

....

....

(6 marks)

Combining Ingredients — 1

1 A test kitchen is making a gravy. Cornflour is added to chicken stock, which forms a **suspension**.

Explain what is meant by the term 'suspension'.

....

....

(2 marks)

2 Raspberry jam can be made from raspberries and sugar.
During cooking, the sugar dissolves in the juice of the raspberries.

a) Name the type of mixture formed when the sugar dissolves
in the raspberry juice.

....

(1 mark)

b) Raspberries contain a small amount of a natural gelling agent called **pectin**.
Describe the function of pectin in making raspberry jam.

....

....

(1 mark)

3 Mayonnaise is an **emulsion**. The ingredients for a basic mayonnaise are listed below.

a) Name the **emulsifier** in mayonnaise.

....

(1 mark)

b) Describe how an emulsion is formed.

....

....

....

....

(2 marks)

| 1 egg yolk |
| 125 ml olive oil |
| 1 tablespoon white wine vinegar |
| half teaspoon salt |
| half teaspoon mustard powder |
| freshly milled pepper |

c) Give one **other** example of a food emulsion.

....

(1 mark)

Combining Ingredients — 2

4 A cake company is trying out a new recipe for a sponge cake.
The main ingredients are flour, sugar, butter and eggs.

a) Give **two** reasons why caster sugar might be used rather than a dark brown sugar.

....

....
(2 marks)

b) Analysis of the cake shows that it is too dense.
Suggest **two** alterations the company could make to fix this problem.

1. ....

2. ....
(2 marks)

c) **i)** The company wants to appeal to consumers on a **calorie-controlled diet**.
They replace the butter in the cake with a low-fat spread.
Suggest **one** effect this may have on the sponge cake.

....
(1 mark)

ii) Describe **one other** way the cake could be altered to appeal to people on low calorie diets.

....
(1 mark)

5 A café is designing a pizza for its new menu. It will be made
using dough, a tomato-based sauce, mozzarella cheese and ham.

a) The tomato sauce used on the pizza lacks flavour.
Suggest **two** ways the flavour of the sauce could be improved.

1. ....

2. ....
(2 marks)

b) The café decides to produce a pizza suitable for people who have a special dietary requirement.

i) Identify **one** diet that they could design a pizza for.

....
(1 mark)

ii) Suggest how the basic ingredients of the pizza could be altered to be suitable for this diet.

....

....
(2 marks)

Standard Food Components — 1

1 Standard components are often used in the production of ready made lasagnes.

a) Explain what is meant by the term 'standard component'.

....
(1 mark)

b) Name **three** standard components a manufacturer could use to make a lasagne product.

1. ....

2. ....

3. ....
(3 marks)

2 A pie company uses standard components in their chicken pies. Identify **two** standard components the company might use and suggest a **different** advantage for using each one.

Standard Component	Advantage

(4 marks)

3 A company that specialises in desserts has recently decided **not** to use standard components, but to use fresh ingredients instead.

a) Give **one** reason why a consumer might prefer to buy a dessert that contains no standard components.

....
(1 mark)

b) Give **three** disadvantages to manufacturers of using standard components in their products.

1. ....

2. ....

3. ....
(3 marks)

Standard Food Components — 2

4 A manufacturer uses pre-made icing and marzipan to decorate their products.

a) Give **three** advantages to the manufacturer of using pre-made icing and marzipan.

....

....

....

....
(3 marks)

b) Name **two** other standard components that can be used in cake production.

1. ....

2. ....
(2 marks)

5 Standard components can affect the **sustainability** of products as well as how much they **cost**.

Make sure you include enough information on both sustainability and cost to get all 7 marks.

a) Evaluate the effect of using standard components on the sustainability and cost of a product.

....

....

....

....

....

....

....

....
(7 marks)

b) Suggest **two** ways a manufacturer could reduce the impact of using standard components on the environment.

....

....
(2 marks)

Scale of Production — 1

1 Continuous flow and one-off are two different types of food production.

a) Give an example of a product that might be made using each production method.

  i) Continuous flow production.

  ....
  (1 mark)

  ii) One-off production.

  ....
  (1 mark)

b) Give **one** advantage and **one** disadvantage of using one-off production.

....

....
  (2 marks)

2 A biscuit manufacturer sells a range of plain and chocolate-coated biscuits to local shops. The biscuits are produced using **batch production**.

a) Explain what is meant by the term 'batch production'.

....
  (1 mark)

b) Explain why batch production is the most suitable production method for the biscuit manufacturer.

....

....

....

....
  (3 marks)

c) The manufacturer is considering using mass production to make the most popular line of chocolate biscuits. Give **one** benefit of using mass production instead of batch production.

....
  (1 mark)

d) Before mass production could start, the production line would have to be changed. Suggest **one** other change the manufacturer would have to make so that the biscuits could be mass produced.

....
  (1 mark)

Scale of Production — 2

3   The picture on the right shows a cereal product designed using **CAD**.

a)   State what 'CAD' stands for.

....
(1 mark)

b)   Give **one** advantage of using CAD to design:

i)   the cereal product,

....

....
(1 mark)

ii)   the product packaging.

....
(1 mark)

Soggy Nut Maizedrops

They're grrrim!!

4   A food manufacturer uses **CAM** during its production process.

a)   State what 'CAM' stands for.

....
(1 mark)

b)   Explain the advantages of using CAM during food production.

....

....

....

....
(3 marks)

5   Give examples of how CAD and CAM could be used in pizza production.

....

....

....

....

....

....
(4 marks)

Quality Control — 1

1   Quality control checks are vital in the manufacturing process.

   a)   Explain what is meant by the term 'quality control'.

....

(1 mark)

   b)   Explain why control checks are important in food production.

....

....

(2 marks)

2   A factory produces thousands of identical loaves of bread a day. Give **two** different control checks that should be used to make sure the product is consistent.

   1. ....

   2. ....

(2 marks)

3   The customer service department at a food company has to deal with customer complaints. Complete the table to show:
   • whether each problem was caused by a biological, physical or chemical contamination,
   • **two** control checks that could be used to prevent each problem.

	Complaint	Type of Contamination	Control checks to prevent problem
a)	False fingernail found in a pie.	....	1. .... 2. ....
b)	Food poisoning after eating a quiche.	....	1. .... 2. ....

(6 marks)

Quality Control — 2

4 Describe **three** different control checks a manufacturer could use when selecting ingredients to produce a high quality fish product.

....

....

....

(3 marks)

5 The flowchart below shows the process of making chocolate muffins. Add notes to the flowchart to describe the control checks you would put in place after each stage of the process.

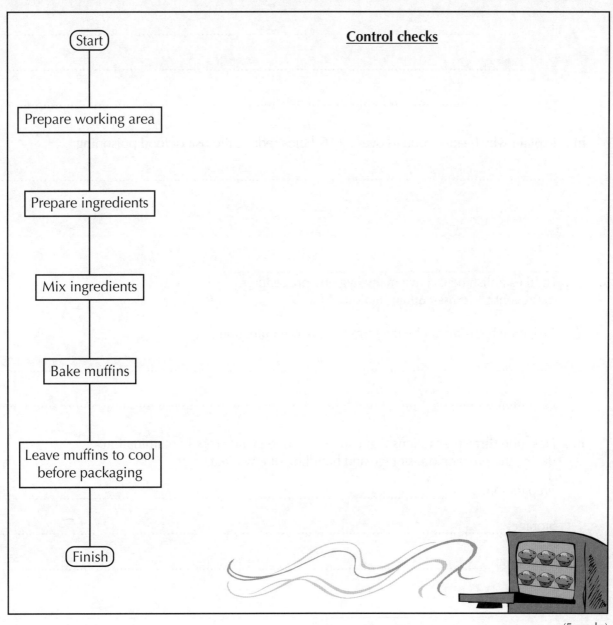

Start

Control checks

Prepare working area

Prepare ingredients

Mix ingredients

Bake muffins

Leave muffins to cool before packaging

Finish

(5 marks)

Section Three — Food Processes

Food Contamination and Bacteria — 1

1 A restaurant serves a prawn cocktail starter. The ingredients are listed on the right. Identify **two** high-risk foods in the prawn cocktail.

1. ....

2. ....

(2 marks)

crispy lettuce

prawns

mayonnaise

salad cream

lemon juice

paprika

If you're not sure of the answer, have a guess — you might just pick up marks.

2 **Food poisoning** can be caused by eating food contaminated with bacteria.

a) Give **three** typical symptoms of food poisoning.

1. ....

2. ....

3. ....

(3 marks)

b) Explain why heating food to over 72 °C helps reduce the risk of food poisoning.

....

(1 mark)

3 Food establishments have many hygiene procedures to prevent the **cross-contamination** of food.

a) Explain what is meant by the term 'cross-contamination'.

....

....

(2 marks)

b) Describe **three** precautions that can be taken to avoid cross-contamination during the preparation, storage and handling of raw meat.

Preparation: ....

Storage: ....

Handling: ....

(3 marks)

Food Contamination and Bacteria — 2

4 A chicken curry is made up of chicken, curry sauce and rice. Chicken and rice are both **high-risk foods**.

a) Explain why chicken is a high-risk food.

....

....

....

....

(3 marks)

b) Give an example of a health and safety procedure you should follow when **serving** chicken curry.

....

....

(1 mark)

c) Complete the table below by describing **two** safety and hygiene procedures a restaurant should follow when purchasing, storing and cooking chicken.

Purchasing chicken	....
Storing chicken	....
Cooking chicken	....

(6 marks)

Preservation — 1

1 Food can be preserved by **heating** it to high temperatures.

a) State the minimum temperature needed to kill bacteria in food.

....

(1 mark)

b) Give **one** example of a preservation method that uses heat.

....

(1 mark)

2 Some foods can be preserved using **additives**.

a) Briefly describe how each of the following additives acts as a preservative.

i) vinegar

....

....

(1 mark)

ii) salt

....

....

(1 mark)

b) Give **one** example of a food product that is preserved using salt.

....

(1 mark)

c) Give **two** disadvantages of using additives to preserve food.

....

....

(2 marks)

3 The temperature range of 5 °C to 63 °C is known as the **danger zone**.
Explain why most foods should **not** be kept at a temperature within the danger zone.

....

....

....

(2 marks)

Preservation — 2

4   Chilling and freezing helps to preserve food.

a)   **i)**   State the two temperatures between which chilled food should be stored.

....

(1 mark)

ii)   Explain why chilling high-risk foods increases their shelf life.

....

(1 mark)

b)   Evaluate the advantages and disadvantages of freezing a product to preserve it.

....

....

....

....

(4 marks)

5   Explain the meaning of the information on the packaging of each of the following products.

a)

BEST BEFORE 01.03.13

Hazelnut chocolates

....

....

....

....

....

(3 marks)

b)

USE BY 01.01.12

Cream-filled doughnuts

....

....

....

....

(3 marks)

Domestic and Industrial Equipment — 1

1   Nutrients are often lost from vegetables when they are boiled.

  a)   Suggest a piece of equipment that can be used to cook vegetables so that fewer nutrients are lost.

....
(1 mark)

  b)   Give another advantage of using the piece of equipment named in **a)**.

....
(1 mark)

2   A wide range of equipment can be used in food preparation.

  a)   Describe how using a temperature probe can help reduce
         the risk of food poisoning when cooking high-risk foods.

                                                            temperature probe

....

....
(2 marks)

  b)   State **three** health and safety precautions that should be followed when using a temperature probe.

....

....

....
(3 marks)

3   For each of the processes given below, suggest **one** piece of electrical
       equipment that could be used and give **two** reasons why.

  a)   Mixing bread dough.

....

....

....
(3 marks)

       b)   Making a tomato purée.

....

....

....

....
(3 marks)

Domestic and Industrial Equipment — 2

4 Manufacturers aim to produce high quality, **consistent** products. Explain how each of the following pieces of equipment can be used to produce consistent products.

a) Biscuit cutters:

....

....

....

....

(2 marks)

Underline the key words in the question to help you focus your answer — you're writing about underlined consistent products here.

b) Microwave:

....

....

....

....

(2 marks)

5 Explain why most industrial manufacturers choose to use computerised weighing equipment to make their products.

....

....

....

....

....

....

....

(4 marks)

Social Issues — 1

1   Products are often targeted at groups of people with **special dietary needs**. For each product listed below, name **one** possible target group and explain how it meets their dietary needs.

Product	Target Group	Reason
Fruit salad	....	....
High energy snack bar	....	....
Calcium-enriched cereal	....	....

(6 marks)

2   A food retailer is designing a range of pre-prepared curry dishes.

a) i) Explain why the retailer might need to research the religions of the target market before designing the products.

....

(1 mark)

ii) Give **one** example of a religion the curry dishes could be adapted to suit.
Explain how a curry dish could be designed to be suitable for people belonging to this religion.

Religion: ....

Design features: ....

....

(3 marks)

b) List three **other social issues** that the retailer should consider when designing the curry dishes.

1. ....

2. ....

3. ....

(3 marks)

Social Issues — 2

3 Social and economic factors affect the design of food products.

In the space below, design a snack product aimed at children.

Annotate your sketch to show why the design would appeal to the target group and how it meets their economic needs. Include information on the following factors:

- cost
- ingredients
- appearance

This question asks you about social and economic needs, so don't write about nutritional needs — you won't get any marks for it.

(4 marks)

4 Sales of fruit have changed over the last 30 years. The table below shows percentage sales of different fruits between 1970 to 2000.

a) Identify **two ways** the sales of fruit have changed between 1970 and 2000.

	1970	1980	1990	2000
Apples	50%	46%	42%	37%
Pears	31%	28%	22%	19%
Mangoes	4%	9%	11%	15%
Coconuts	6%	7%	9%	12%
Pineapples	9%	10%	16%	17%

....

....

....

....

(2 marks)

b) Suggest reasons for these changes.

....

....

(2 marks)

Environmental Issues — 1

1   Snazzy Sarnies is a food company that is aiming to make its manufacturing processes more **sustainable**. One of their products is shown below.

a) **i)** Explain what is meant by the term 'sustainable'.

....

....
(1 mark)

Plastic packaging — White bread — Bluefin tuna — Mayonnaise
Cardboard packaging — Lettuce

Tuna, Lettuce and Mayo

ii) Give **two** reasons why the product shown on the right might **not** be sustainable.

....

....

....
(2 marks)

b) **i)** One way Snazzy Sarnies could make more sustainable products is to reduce the food miles of their ingredients. Explain what is meant by the term 'food miles'.

....
(1 mark)

ii) Give one **advantage** to the company, **other** than improving sustainability, of reducing the food miles of their ingredients.

....
(1 mark)

c) Suggest **two** other ways that Snazzy Sarnies could make their products more sustainable.

....

....
(2 marks)

2   **Animal welfare** and **fair trade** are both ethical issues associated with food production.

a) Describe **two** ways that food may be labelled to show that animal welfare has been considered during food production.

1. ....

2. ....
(2 marks)

b) Some food carries the FAIRTRADE Mark. Explain what this mark means.

....

....
(2 marks)

Section Four — Marketing and Environment

Environmental Issues — 2

3 The table below shows how sales of **organic** and **non-organic** vegetables have changed in Byrnshire between 1980 and 2005.

Year	Organic vegetables (tonnes)	Non-organic vegetables (tonnes)
1980	127	840
1985	150	820
1990	171	801
1995	193	786
2000	258	712
2005	295	698

a) i) Describe how the type of vegetables sold in Byrnshire has changed between 1980 and 2005. Suggest reasons for these changes in sales.

....

....

....

....

(4 marks)

b) i) Describe **one** disadvantage to the **farmer** of growing organic food.

....

(1 mark)

ii) Describe **one** disadvantage to the **consumer** of buying organic food.

....

(1 mark)

4 Some people believe that shops should only stock **local, seasonal food**. Evaluate the advantages and disadvantages of only using local, seasonal food.

....

....

....

....

....

(4 marks)

Labelling — 1

1   The **nutritional information** below is from the label of a snack product.

a)   State how many grams of fat are found in
100 g of the snack product.

....
(1 mark)

b)   The manufacturer decides to label the
snack as 'low-fat'. State whether this is a
reasonable claim and explain your answer.

....

....

....
(2 marks)

NUTRITIONAL INFORMATION		
	per 100 g	per 40 g serving
Energy	2180kJ/525 kcal	872kJ/210 kcal
Protein	6.5 g	2.6 g
Carbohydrate	50.0 g	20.0 g
of which sugars	2.0 g	0.8 g
Fat	33.0 g	13.2 g
of which saturates	15.0 g	6.0 g
Sodium	0.7 g	0.3 g
Fibre	4.0 g	1.6 g

2   Symbols on labels can provide a wide range of information about the product.

State the meaning of the symbols below. Give **two** reasons why each symbol is useful.

a) **V**	....
b) **!** **May contain nuts**	....
c) ♲	....

(9 marks)

Labelling — 2

3   The labels on pre-packed food products are required by **law** to provide consumers with certain pieces of information.

a) **i)** Explain why some labels require a 'use by date' on their labels, whilst others only have a 'best before date'.

....

....

(2 marks)

ii) Name **one** product that requires a 'use by date', and **one** that requires a 'best before date'.

Use by date: ....

Best before date: ....

(2 marks)

b) In the space below, sketch a design for a label to go on a pre-prepared cottage pie. Your sketch should show all the information that is required by law to be on the product. Annotate your sketch to explain the information shown on the label.

(8 marks)

__Packaging — 1__

1   Food is often packaged before it is sold. Give three **functions** of packaging.

    1. ....

    2. ....

    3. ....

(3 marks)

2   Look at the picture below, which shows the inner and outer packaging of a breakfast cereal.

a) **i)** Name the material that the outer box is made from.

    ....

(1 mark)

    ii) Describe the advantages and disadvantages of
    using this material to package the product.

    Advantages: ....

inner packet   outer box

    ....

    ....

    Disadvantages: ....

    ....

(4 marks)

b) Name the material that the inner packet is made from.

....

(1 mark)

c) The sustainability of product packaging must be considered during product design.
Evaluate the sustainability of the packaging materials you named in **a)** and **b)**.

....

....

....

....

....

....

(4 marks)

Packaging — 2

3 Study the four food products shown below.

Milk

Cheese

Crisps

Meat

a) Choose **two** of the products shown above.
Name and describe a type of packaging that would help to extend the shelf life of each.
Choose a **different** type of packaging for each product.

Product 1: ....

Packaging: ....

....

Product 2: ....

Packaging: ....

....

(4 marks)

b) i) Nanotechnology can improve the packaging of food products.
Describe what is meant by nanotechnology.

....

(1 mark)

ii) Choose **one** of the products shown above.
Suggest **two** ways that nanotechnology could be used in the packaging of this product.

Product: ....

1. ....

....

2. ....

....

(4 marks)

iii) Describe what effect the use of nanotechnology is likely to have on the cost of the packaging.

....

(1 mark)

Packaging — 3

(5 marks)

4 Sensational Sauces Ltd. is designing the packaging for a new pasta sauce product. The initial design idea is shown below.

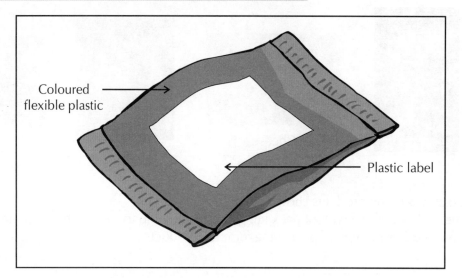

Coloured flexible plastic

Plastic label

Analysis of the design suggests that the packaging **isn't sustainable**.

In the space below, sketch an improved design for the packaging. Your packaging design should be suitable for pasta sauce and be more sustainable than the packaging shown above.

Annotate your sketch to explain your design choices.

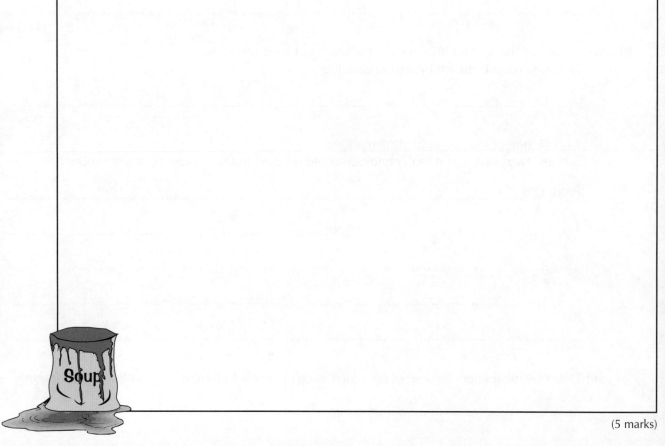

Soup

TFAW42

(5 marks)